Peppa Pig™

The Wishing Well

Grandpa Pig is showing Peppa and George
his plants. He is very proud of his garden.
"What is this, Grandpa?" asks Peppa.
"It's a weed," replies Grandpa. "A cheeky plant
growing in the wrong spot. We must get rid of it!"

"This little plastic gnome is going to live in our garden," says Granny Pig. "His name is Mr Gnome."

"Oh no he isn't!" snorts Grandpa. "I can't have that funny thing looking at me all day!"

"Peppa and George," says Granny, "do you think Mr Gnome looks funny?"

"No, Granny," replies
Peppa. "I think he
looks cute."
"Cute!" agrees George.
"You're outnumbered,
I'm afraid, Grandpa,"
cries Granny.
"Mr Gnome is staying
in the garden!"

Toot, Toot!

Just then, Mr Bull arrives with a truck full of gnomes. "Gardens are for plants, not plastic!" Grandpa tells Mr Bull. "We don't want gnomes!"
"But these are Granny's gnomes," says Peppa.
"Oh! It appears we do want gnomes," says Grandpa.
"Okey-dokey," says Mr Bull, tipping the gnomes on to the grass.

Clang!
Clatter!

Peppa, George and Granny Pig stare at the enormous pile of gnomes. They make the garden look messy. "Wow!" says Peppa. "They are lovely." But Grandpa Pig doesn't think so.

"I have this for you, too," says Mr Bull, giving Granny and Grandpa Pig a big box.

"Thank you, Mr Bull," says Granny.
"That must be my plastic well."
"What's the point of a well without
water?" asks Grandpa.

"It's a wishing well,"
says Granny.
"You throw a coin into
it, and make a wish."
"Do the wishes come
true, Granny?"
asks Peppa.

"Yes!" says Granny.
"Ooh, can I make a
wish?" Peppa asks.
"Of course, Peppa,"
replies Granny,
giving Peppa and
George a coin each.

Peppa and George throw their coins into the well and make a wish.

Later, Peppa tells Grandpa Pig what they wished for. "We wished that we could have a wishing well and gnomes in our garden, too!" "Oh," says Grandpa. "I think we can make that wish come true!"

Splish!

Grandpa Pig drives Peppa and George
home to Mummy and Daddy Pig.
"Mummy! Daddy!" cries Peppa.
"I made a wish and it came true!"

"What did you wish for, Peppa?" asks Daddy Pig.
"Lots of gnomes and a wishing well for
our garden!" cries Peppa.

"I don't think we have enough room for all of those gnomes!" says Mummy Pig, looking at the big pile Grandpa is carrying.
"Nonsense!" replies Grandpa.
"You've got plenty of room!"

"Oh," says Daddy Pig, uncertainly. "I suppose we do."

The gnomes and the wishing well take up the whole
of the garden! Peppa and George are very happy.
And Grandpa Pig is very happy, too!